Your Inner Compass That Could

Kristin Pierce

Dedication:

For my sweet, adventurous, inspiring little souls:
Aspen and Kendrix — May you confidently follow
your Inner Compass wherever it leads.
For my husband, Matt — Thank you for always believing in me.

Foreword:

Your Inner Compass is a device for finding direction.

North, South, East, West - Uncover the internal connection.

Feel the pull of True North with pure fascination.

This Compass is your tool for soul navigation.

You are the one who knows your true self the best.
You have an Inner Compass inside of your chest.
If you learn how to listen, it will be your best guide,
On life's wonderful, magical, adventurous ride.

From deep in your heart,
your compass will lead you by feel,
And show you the way
to being authentically real.

When something feels heavy or when it feels light,
Your Compass is showing you what's wrong and what's right...
Just for you on your path - trust within - don't be nervous.
The messages are profound if you allow them to surface.

To make good decisions
and be very smart,
Just follow the compass
inside your heart.

You don't have to remain
on the straight and narrow.
Be true to yourself
and follow your own arrow.

Find what excites you
and a spark will ignite.
Fuel this fire deep inside you
to spread your light.

The spark in your eyes
will be proof you've discovered
Your passion, your purpose,
your best self being uncovered.

Don't hide your blazing light -
don't try to resist.
Once you've found your True North,
let it insist...

On leading your way
through the ups and the downs,
And your intuition will grow
by leaps and by bounds.

Be brave enough to sing the song in your soul.
It will pave your path to step into your truest role.

Keep moving forward in following your desire,
And you'll continue to fuel your inspired inner fire.

Remember that you can
always change your mind.
You are never confined,
even when you are in a bind.

Life is about learning
no matter the cost.
If you follow your Compass,
you will never have lost.

Mistakes are for learning
as long as you grow.
So, keep on creating
your best life as you go.

You can always go back
to take the fork in the road;
Align with your heart's song —
it will lighten the load.

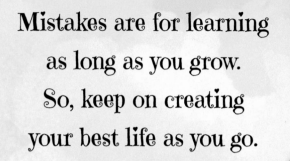

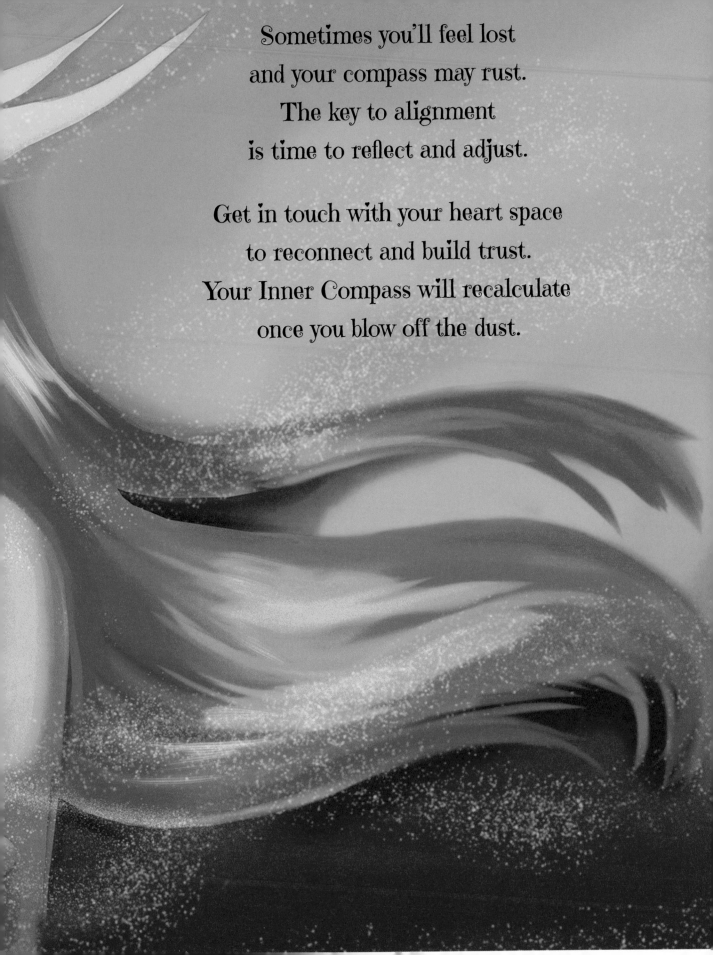

Sometimes you'll feel lost
and your compass may rust.
The key to alignment
is time to reflect and adjust.

Get in touch with your heart space
to reconnect and build trust.
Your Inner Compass will recalculate
once you blow off the dust.

The wisdom within you is more precious than gold. Give it quiet attention and its voice will grow bold.

No one else can decide
what you choose to pursue.
Find what fills you up
to illuminate your true avenue.

Deep down, only you
can find fulfillment within.
You decide your fate
for the ultimate win.

You're as unique as a snowflake —
you are one-of-a-kind.
You have an unmatched perspective
and a powerful mind.

There is no one else like you
on the face of the Earth.
Fearlessly share your talents;
graciously give your worth.

You can conquer the world
and accomplish your dreams.
You have unlimited possibilities
and a supportive team.

There is no need to compare
your life's path to another's.
Your Inner Compass is meant
to guide you and no other.

There are no limits to what you can achieve.
So, make your own rules and make sure you believe.

Any steps taken forward are better than none.
Let your journey create an abundance of fun!

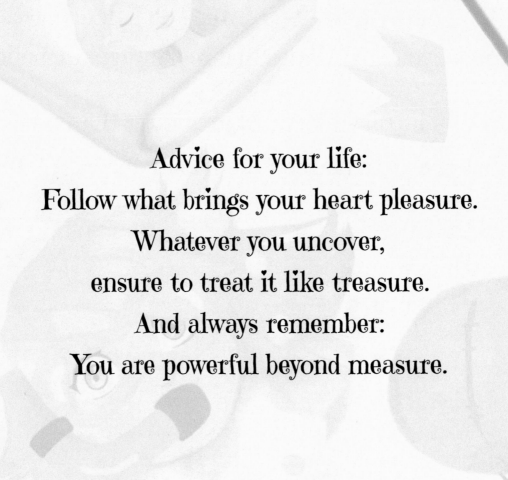

Advice for your life:
Follow what brings your heart pleasure.
Whatever you uncover,
ensure to treat it like treasure.
And always remember:
You are powerful beyond measure.

Integration Questions:

What are the ways in which your Inner Compass can communicate with you?

In what ways do you notice your own Inner Compass sending you messages?

Why can it sometimes be hard to hear these messages from within?

What happens when you have a gut feeling or an inner knowing about something, but don't listen to it? How does it feel?

What happens when you act on a gut feeling or listen to a quiet message from within? How could making decisions in this way potentially benefit you?

How can you encourage the messages from your Inner Compass to grow stronger?

Reflect on a time when you were so excited about something that you couldn't stop talking about it. What topics light you up with passion and enthusiasm?

Integration Questions:

Reflect on a mistake you have made from which you gained a great learning message.

Could you revisit other mistakes or misunderstandings
to uncover deeper learning and growth?

Has there ever been a time when you needed to go back to the fork in the road
and readjust your decision to make it feel better aligned in your heart?

How big would you dream if you knew that absolutely anything was possible?

You are unique. "There is no one else like you on the face of the Earth." What
special gifts and talents do you have that you could share with the world?

What possibilities would you hope to find if you discovered
your own Door of Unlimited Possibilities?

For Creative Integration Activities, along with a Parent and Teacher Resource,
visit www.InnerCompassBooks.com

About the Author:

Photo by Nancy Newby Photography

After a cosmic hammer experience with cancer at the age of 21, Kristin realized there was a big piece she had been missing and ignoring within herself. Embarking down a new road of consciousness-based healthcare, through a journey of deep introspection and inner evolution, (along with many other adventures) she realized a profound message that needed to be shared.

Inspired by her two young children and the immense inner wisdom that lies inside each of us, Kristin was eager to open minds to incredible power of one's inner knowing. In sharing this book, she hopes to encourage adults and children, alike, to trust their truest guide by listening to the messages from within. She teaches workshops across Canada, works with clients around the world, leads online programs for awakened awaresnesss, and is always creating awareness-evoking goodness.

Kristin lives in Warman, Saskatchewan, Canada with her husband, two children, and their dog.

To learn more, visit www.InnerCompassBooks.com
or www.InnerCompassAcademy.com

Tellwell Talent

www.tellwell.ca

ISBN

978-1-77370-803-4 (Hardcover)

978-1-77370-802-7 (Paperback)

If you loved this book, please help us spread
the Inner Compass word!

Find us on Facebook @InnerCompassBooks

Stay tuned for more self-published magic at
www.InnerCompassBooks.com